Draw it with th
ARTBOX
BUNCH

Tony Hart

BBC CHiLDRENS BOOKS

This book is based on the BBC Children's TV series
The Artbox Bunch
Executive Producer: Christopher Pilkington

Published by BBC Children's Books,
a division of BBC Enterprises Limited,
Woodlands, 80 Wood Lane, London W12 0TT

First published 1995

ISBN 0 563 40388 8

Typeset by BBC Children's Books
Cover printed by Clays Ltd, St Ives plc
Printed and bound in Great Britain by Ebenezer Baylis Ltd, Worcester

Contents

Getting Started

Anyone can draw – it's just a case of knowing how to get started.

All the drawings in this book are based on simple shapes, such as circles, rectangles and triangles. You begin each picture by drawing the shapes in pencil, step by step. Once this outline is drawn, you'll be ready to draw the finished picture in ink over the pencil lines. Then rub out the pencil lines and the picture is ready for colouring.

You don't need much special equipment – in fact, you can do everything in this book with just a pencil, a fine-tip pen, a rubber and some colour pens. However, you might find it helps to have some other members of the Artbox Bunch too, to help out with the tricky bits . . .

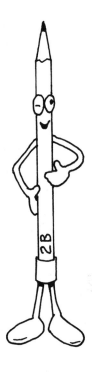

Use a **Pencil** for the first shapes. Soft 2B pencils are best. They make a strong line, but will rub out easily once you've done the finished drawing.

Rubbers are essential for rubbing out mistakes and pencil sketches.

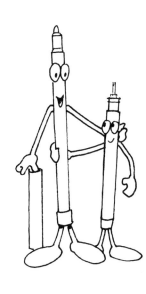

A **fine-tip permanent marker pen** is best for making the finished drawing. **Felt-tip pens** and **paint sticks** are good for colouring in.

There are special spaces on each page for you to make your drawings, but you might also want to do them on sheets of **paper**. Photocopier paper, in A4 size, is usually the best value.

Use **compasses** for drawing circles exactly.

Use a **ruler f**or difficult straight lines.

The best way to keep your pencils sharp is to use a **pencil sharpener**.

You can also use **water colours** or **marker pens** to colour your drawings or paint coloured backgrounds for them.

Scissors will come in handy for cutting out pictures. Or you could cut and fold your drawings to turn them into cards.

Penguin Portrait

With a soft pencil, draw two ovals – the body and the head.

Add triangles for the feet and tail.

Finally, draw a line at the beak and diamond for the flipper.

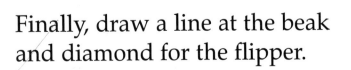

Take a fine-tip marker pen and draw the penguin on top of your outline shapes. Shade in the dark parts of the body – and don't forget to give your penguin an eye!

Try drawing your own penguin at home amongst the icebergs.

Don't worry if you don't get the shapes exactly right at first. You can always rub them out and start again.

Smart Soldier

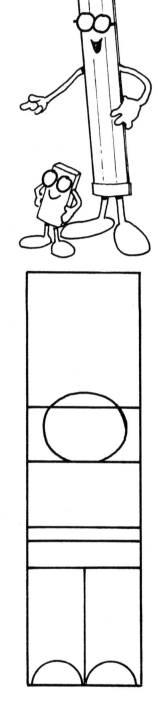

This smart soldier contains a lot of straight lines.
You might need some help from a ruler here.

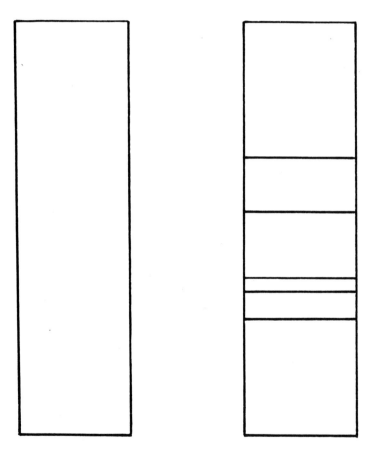

Start by drawing a simple box shape.

Add lines across the box.

Put in the circle shape for the head, and lines for the trousers and feet.

Give the finished soldier arms,
a gun, buttons and a smile.

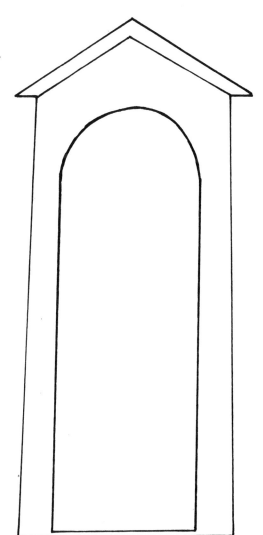

Put a soldier in the sentry box.
Try another one in front of
this castle.

Stegosaurus

Begin with a circle and an oval.

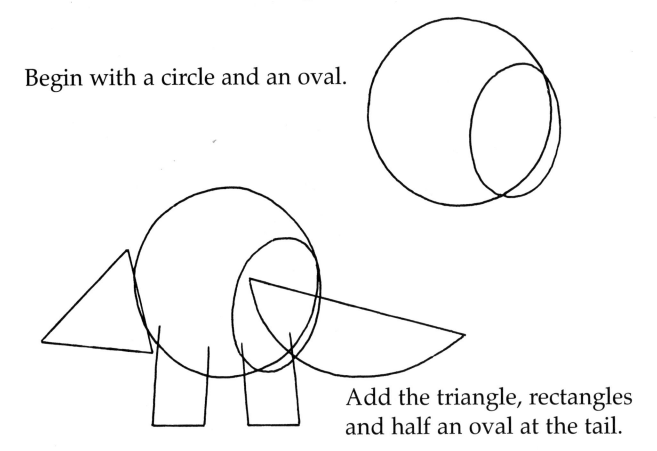

Add the triangle, rectangles and half an oval at the tail.

Put in ovals at the head, and circles where the dinosaur's plates will go. Then add lines for the tail.

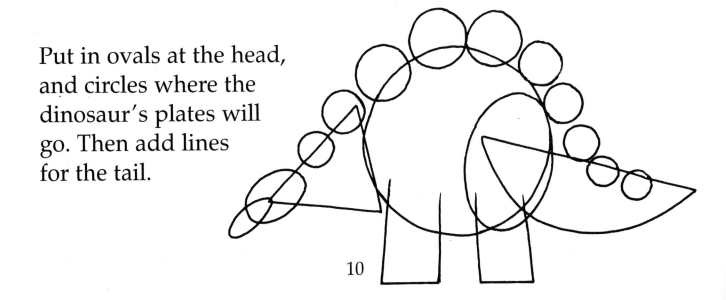

10

Draw the finished body shape first, and then add the plates to the Stegosaurus's back.

Put a finished dinosaur in this misty, prehistoric landscape. Or you could paint your own background of weird, prehistoric plants.

Ship Ahoy!

This ship picture uses a lot of box shapes.

Start by drawing a long thin rectangle.

Shape the ends of the rectangle and
add a wavy line for the sea.

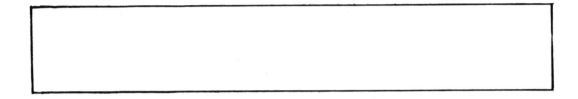

Put in the other box shapes
and lines.

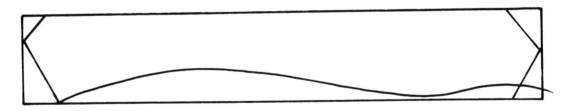

Give the finished ship
a radar and portholes.

Put the ship out to sea. You could draw your own
background, perhaps with some seagulls – and
make the sea either calm or stormy.

Jungle Tigers

Here are two jungle tigers for you to try –
a cub and a parent. Once you've perfected
your drawings, you can include them both
in the jungle scene over the page.

Cub

Start off with a box and an oval.

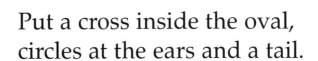

Put a cross inside the oval,
circles at the ears and a tail.

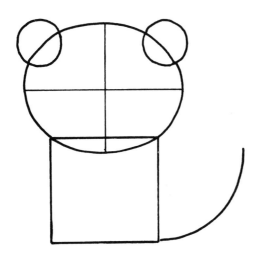

As you make your finished
drawing, the cross will help
you get the tiger's eyes, nose
and mouth in the right place.

14

Parent

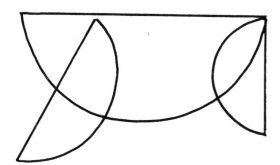

Begin with three half-moon shapes.

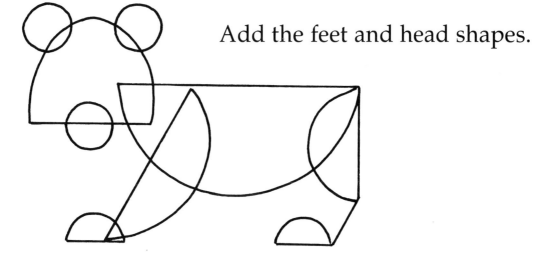

Add the feet and head shapes.

Shade in the tiger's stripes with your marker pen.

15

In the Jungle

Here's a giant jungle scene. Put a tiger and cub on the ground and a parrot and toucan in the trees.

Birds of Paradise

These are two more animals for the jungle picture.

Toucan

Draw two almond shapes, overlapping at one edge.

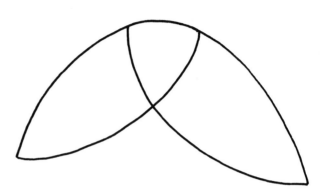

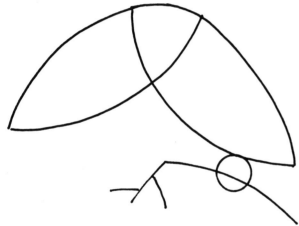

Add a circle at the claws and lines for the branches.

The toucan has a colourful stripy beak and a black and white body.

Parrot

Start the parrot with
four oval shapes.

Put in lines for the
tail feathers and circles
at the claws.

Following the pencil shapes,
draw an outline of the parrot's
body in marker pen. Then fill in
the feathers on the wing.

Make your parrot
as brightly coloured
as you can.

19

Speed Machine

Just like the ship, this fast car
starts off with a long box shape.

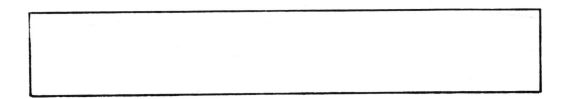

Add circles at the wheels.

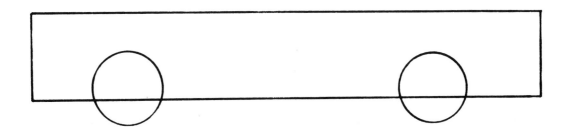

Draw an arc on top of the box and a sloping line inside it.

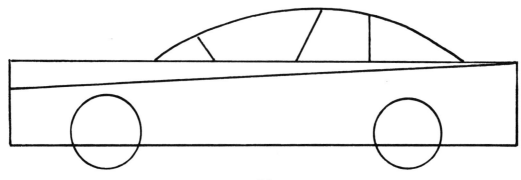

When you make your finished drawing, put in a steering wheel, petrol cap and some go-faster stripes – and if yours is a rally car, it might need a number on the side too.

Draw your own car, speeding past these houses and shops.

Leaping Dolphin

Make this friendly dolphin look
as graceful as you can.

Begin with two oval shapes.

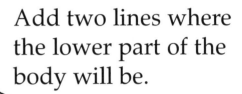

Add two lines where
the lower part of the
body will be.

Put in the shapes for
the fins and flippers.

Shade your finished dolphin
where it has glistening
black markings.

Draw the dolphin so that it is leaping out of the ocean.

You could make your own giant sea picture. First paint a
background of the sea. Then draw this dolphin, a ship and
the penguin on an iceberg, cut them all out and stick them
down on the background.

Flower Show

Buttercup

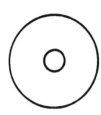  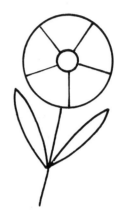

Draw two circles – a small one inside a large one.

Divide the circles into five equal sections.

Add leaf and stalk lines.

Draw one petal inside each of the sections of the circle.

Daffodil

Draw three intersecting lines.

Add the bell shape and lines for the stalk and leaves.

Put in the shapes for the bee.

Draw one petal around each
of the intersecting lines.

Make your own flower show picture. You could try to
invent some other flowers of your own.

Mosque

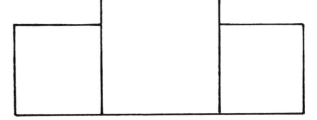

Draw a large square, with two slightly smaller squares attached to opposite sides.

Draw a line through the middle of the square, and make a circle with the same line in the middle.

Use a ruler and compass if you want to get the measurements exactly right.

Add long thin rectangles at each edge for the towers, and put a small circle at the top of each.

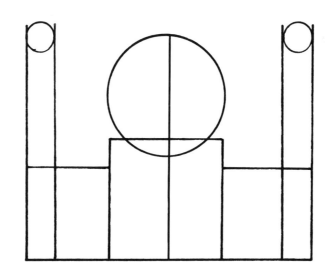

26

When you make the finished picture, the circles will help you to draw good, even minarets.

Put a mosque inside this oasis, surrounded by palm trees. You could also draw a mosque in a busy town scene.

Flying High

Lift off with this helicopter picture.

Start with an oval and two long lines that meet at the tail.

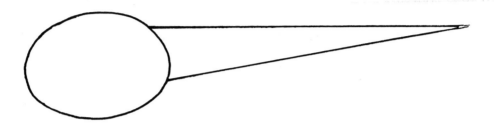

Add more lines for the tail, blades and cabin.

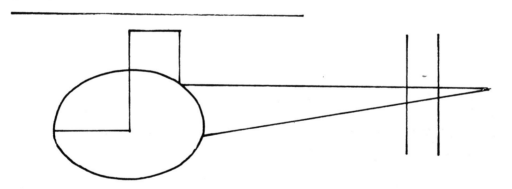

Put in the final lines and box shapes.

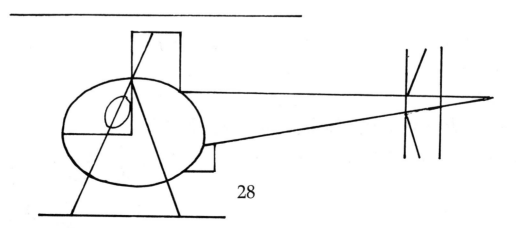

28

Decorate the body of the helicopter with a stripy pattern and its registration letters – and don't forget the pilot!

Draw your own helicopter hovering above this airport.

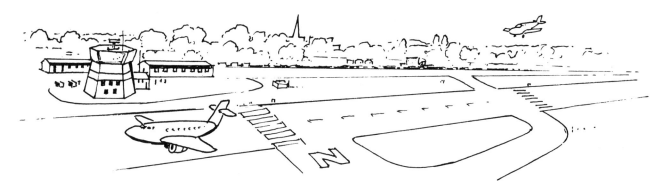

You could draw a helicopter on a piece of paper and cut it out. Then, in an old magazine, find a picture with lots of sky, cut that out too, and paste down your helicopter so that it's flying across the sky in the photograph.

29

Grinning Alligator

This alligator has a big grin – but is he really as friendly as he looks?

Draw a circle for the head and an oval for the body.

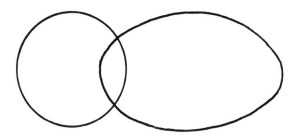

Add lines for the tail.

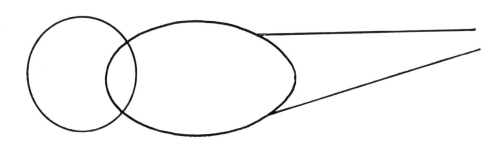

Put in circles and half-moon shapes for the legs, eyes and jaws.

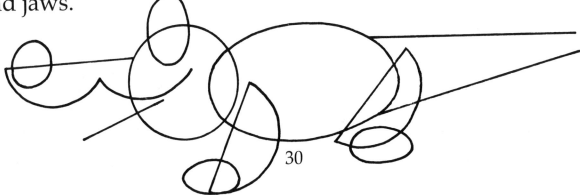

Draw some scales down your alligator's back and give him a cunning smile.

Put your own alligator on this swampy riverbank.

The Next Step...

Once you've finished working through the drawings in this book, you can start experimenting – with different pens, crayons, paints and markers. You might want to experiment with whole new drawings and shapes of your own too.

Remember – most illustrators make rough pencil drawings before they use ink. And whatever you decide to do, always have fun with your drawing. Just like the Artbox Bunch!